I love you the way you are ...

... now and forever, with all my wild heart.

I love you the way the sun sets ...

... this day and every day.

I love you the way the great mountain stands ...

... unshakable, unquakable!

I love you the way the clouds drift ...

... drowsy and dreamy.